# The stories at this level

These stories are still centred round the people your child has the fun and security of meeting t These characters are also shown reading their c their parents. The West Street 'children' like reading fairy stories, rhymes and legends. This emphasises how much all children enjoy reading and sharing stories with their parents, and how much this is a normal part of everyday life. It will also encourage your children to share their own enjoyment of the characters coming to life in these stories.

Before you start reading the book with your child, read the story and activities first yourself, so that you become familiar with the text and the best way to give it expression and emphasis when reading it aloud.

Always sit comfortably with your child, so that both of you can see the book easily. Read the story, making it sound as interesting as possible. Encourage your child to participate actively in the reading, to turn over the pages and to become involved in the story and characters. You may find that your child is ready to share in the reading more quickly than before.

Sometimes let your children look through the book before you start reading, and for a change, let them guess what the story is about from the pictures. Encourage them to talk about the pictures, and add your own suggestions, if you wish, to help them with the story line.

This may be enough for one sitting, but don't give your child the idea that the book is finished with. Encourage your child to take the book away and to look through it alone, to find any bits that either of you particularly enjoyed.

Next time you look at the book with your child, suggest "Let's read the story together. You join in with me. If you want to go on reading on your own, give my arm a little push (or any other signal you prefer), and I'll stop reading and you go on. Give me another push when you want me to join in with you again." Let your child follow the words with a finger *under* them. Don't stop to repeat or correct words: keep the interest up and the story flowing along.

The next time you both look at the book, have a quick chat about the contents of the story, then invite your child to read it to you without you reading as well. Give help with words or phrases that cause difficulty. Join in with the reading again if your child is struggling with the story.

## The activities at this level

The activities at the back of the book need not be completed at once. They are not a test, but will help your child to remember the words and stories and to develop further the skills required for becoming a fluent reader.

The activities are often divided into three parts:

One part is designed to encourage you both to talk about the stories, and to link them where possible with your child's own experiences. Encourage your child to predict what will happen and to recall the main events of the story. Change the wording of the story as much as you like and encourage your children to tell you about the story in their own way.

One part encourages children to look back through the book to find general or specific things in the text or the pictures. Your child learns to begin to look at the text itself, and to recognise individual words and letters more precisely. The activities state clearly when you should give a letter its name, and when you should sound it out. The activities also introduce more writing, largely copying from words in the original story. If your children find this too difficult, copy the words onto a piece of paper for them to trace over.

One part includes activities which your child can do without your help. It may be necessary, though, to read the instructions to your child, pointing out the words as you do so. Read the instructions to the *first* activity only in this way. Then say "Would you like to try this on your own?" One activity at a time is probably enough for your child to do in one sitting.

When all the activities have been done, encourage your child to read the story again before you move on to another book. Your child should now feel secure with it and enjoy reading to you.

# Sleeping Beauty

## by Helen Arnold

### Illustrated by Sara Silcock and Tony Kenyon

A Piccolo Original
In association with Macmillan Education

Will you read me a story
please, Mum?

What do you want me to read?

This book — Sleeping Beauty.

Oh yes, Tamla.
I like that book.

7

There was a princess long ago,
Long ago, long ago.
There was a princess long ago,
Long, long ago.

The princess lived in a big high tower,
A big high tower, a big high tower.
The princess lived in a big high tower,
A big high tower.

12

One day a fairy waved her wand,
Waved her wand, waved her wand.
One day a fairy waved her wand,
Waved her wand.

The princess slept for a hundred years,
A hundred years, a hundred years.
The princess slept for a hundred years,
A hundred years.

A great big forest grew and grew,
Grew and grew, grew and grew.
A great big forest grew and grew,
Grew all around.

A gallant prince came riding by,
Came riding by, came riding by.
A gallant prince came riding by,
Came riding by.

He took his sword and cut the trees,
Cut the trees, cut the trees.
He took his sword and cut the trees,
Cut down the trees.

He took her hand to wake her up,
To wake her up, to wake her up.
He took her hand to wake her up,
To wake her up.

So everyone is happy now,
Happy now, happy now.
So everyone is happy now,
Happy now.

I like that story.

Let's read it again.

# Things to talk about with your children

Can you remember what happened in the story of Sleeping
Beauty?
    Why did the princess go to sleep?
    How did the prince save her?
    Did the story have a happy ending?

## Looking at pictures and words
## with your children

**1.** Can you read these sentences to me?

A great big forest grew and grew.

He took her hand to wake her up.

One day a fairy waved her wand.

There was a princess long ago.

Now can you read them again, this time in the same order as
they are in the story?

**2.** Make four cards as follows:

```
1  ___  ___  ___  ___  ___
```

```
2  ___  ___  ___  ___  ___  ___
```

```
3  ___  ___  ___  ___  ___  ___  ___  ___
```

```
4  ___  ___  ___  ___  ___  ___
```

Give out the cards and ask your child to find the answers in the story to these questions, and then to copy the answers onto the appropriate card.

1. What was big and high?
2. Who came riding by?
3. Who went to sleep?
4. What grew and grew?

Your child might like to draw pictures of the answers and place the cards under the right pictures.

**3.** How many times can you find this word in the story?

big

How many times can you find this word in the story?

riding

How many times can you find this word in the story?

trees

**4.** Write these phrases on a piece of paper. Allow some space on the right for the page numbers to be filled in:

waved her wand    Page

happy now    Page

read me a story    Page

took his sword    Page

a gallant prince    Page

Ask your child to find the page on which each phrase appears and to write it down by the appropriate phrase.

| These activities and skills: | will help your children to: |
|---|---|
| Looking and remembering | hold a story in their heads, retell it in their own words. |
| Listening, being able to tell the difference between sounds | remember sounds in words and link spoken words with the words they see in print. |
| Naming things and using different words to explain or retell events | recognise different words in print, build their vocabulary and guess at the meaning of words. |
| Matching, seeing patterns, similarities and differences | recognise letters, see patterns within words, use the patterns to read 'new' words and split long words into syllables. |
| Knowing the grammatical patterns of spoken language | guess the word-order in reading. |
| Anticipating what is likely to happen next in a story | guess what the next sentence or event is likely to be about. |
| Colouring, getting control of pencils and pens, copying and spelling | produce their own writing, which will help them to understand the way English is written. |
| Understanding new experiences by linking them to what they already know | read with understanding and think about what they have read. |
| Understanding their own feelings and those of others | enjoy and respond to stories and identify with the characters. |

First published 1988 by Pan Books Ltd, Cavaye Place, London SW10 9PG

9 8 7 6 5 4 3 2 1

Editorial consultant: Donna Bailey

© Pan Books Ltd and Macmillan Publishers Ltd 1988. Text © Helen Arnold 1988

British Library Cataloguing in Publication Data
Arnold, Helen
Sleeping Beauty. — (Read together. Level 3).
I. Title  II. Series
428.6        PE1119
ISBN 0–330–30219–1

Printed in Hong Kong